BEWARE!

**Mortimer's madcap
plans and crazy ideas
could rub off on you!**

First published in 2015 by Hodder Children's Books

Text copyright © Tim Healey 2015
Illustrations copyright © Chris Mould 2015

Hodder Children's Books, 338 Euston Road, London, NW1 3BH
Hodder Children's Books Australia, Level 17/207 Kent Street, Sydney, NSW 2000

The right of Tim Healey to be identified as the author and Chris Mould
as the illustrator of this Work has been asserted by them in accordance
with the Copyright, Designs and Patents Act 1988.

A catalogue record of this book is available from the British Library.

ISBN 978 1 444 91969 1

Printed in China

Hodder Children's Books is a division of Hachette Children's Books,
an Hachette UK Company

www.hachette.co.uk

MORTYMER KEENE

DINO DANGER

Tim Healey and Chris Mould

Mr Hart

Age: 31
Special features:
gym teacher, very fit
Weak point: always wears
same tracksuit
Favourite phrase:
'Hup, two, three, four…'

Mortimer Keene

Age: 8
Special features: specs
Weak point: none!
Favourite phrase:
'I have something
to show you…'

Edmontosaurus

Age: 78 million
Special features:
duck bill
Weak point:
doesn't say much
Favourite phrase:
'Quack!'

Anthony Lewis

Age: 7
Special features:
new boy
Weak point:
panics easily
Favourite phrase:
'Do something,
Mortimer!'

SAINT BARNABAS
S B
SCHOOL

Tyrannosaurus

Age: 99 million
Special features:
sharp teeth
Weak point:
no regard for
others' feelings
Favourite phrase:
'Fancy a bite?'

SAINT BARNABAS
S B
SCHOOL

Pterosaur

Age: 63 million
Special features:
huge wings
Weak point:
rubbish at walking
Favourite phrase:
'Flying tonight!'

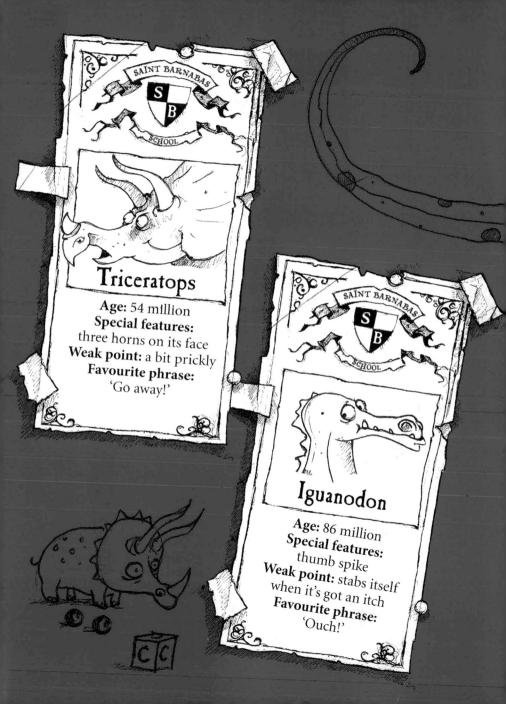

SAINT BARNABAS SCHOOL

Triceratops

Age: 54 million
Special features:
three horns on its face
Weak point: a bit prickly
Favourite phrase:
'Go away!'

SAINT BARNABAS SCHOOL

Iguanodon

Age: 86 million
Special features:
thumb spike
Weak point: stabs itself
when it's got an itch
Favourite phrase:
'Ouch!'

Part One

I have something to show you,
Said Mortimer Keene,
As he proudly uncovered
His new Time Machine.

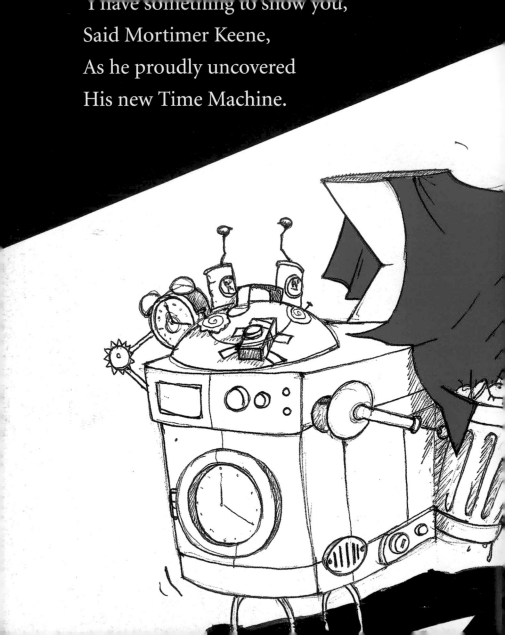

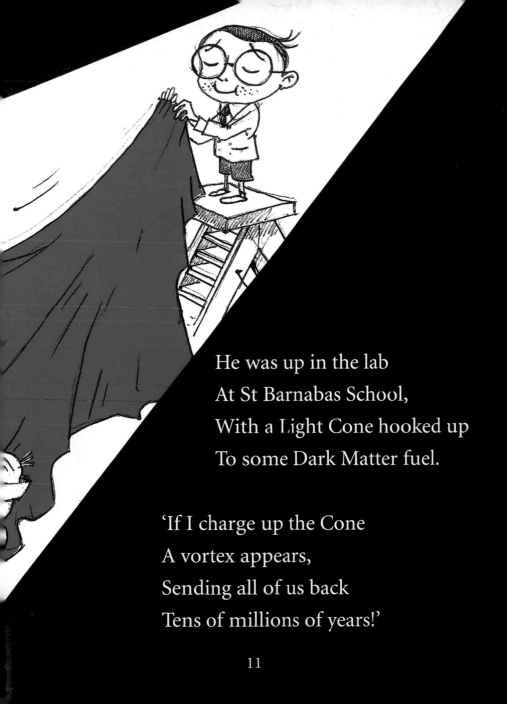

He was up in the lab
At St Barnabas School,
With a Light Cone hooked up
To some Dark Matter fuel.

'If I charge up the Cone
A vortex appears,
Sending all of us back
Tens of millions of years!'

'Don't touch that machine!'

Shrieked young Mr Bevan.
(The man who taught *Shakespeare*
To kids from Year Seven.)

'No worries,' Mortimer
Said with a cough,
'I do know the dangers;
I'll keep it switched off…'

It was break time below,
The kids on the loose,
And there, playing marbles,
Was Emily Bruce.

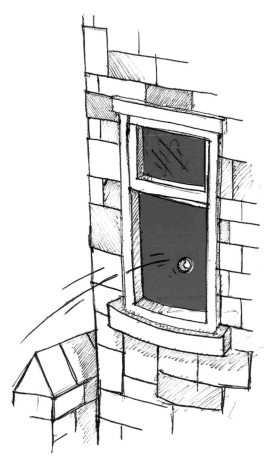

She played her best shot.
But there was a hitch –
It bounced in and set off
The Dark Matter switch!

And something went

FOOMF!

The whole lab now sank
Into a vortex,
And then all went blank…

Part Two

'DINOSAURS! DINOSAURS!'

Shrieked Mr Green,
Numb with amazement
At what he'd just seen.

Around the school building
All was transformed
Into forests and swamps
Where reptilians swarmed!

Lizard-like monsters
With long necks and tails,
Horns, spikes and knobbles,
And great armoured scales.

'DINOSAURS! DINOSAURS!'

Mrs MacNee
Exploded, and dropped
A whole tray of hot tea.

'There's an **IGUANODON!**'
Gasped Mr James,
Who was proud of his knowledge
Of dinosaur names.

'And the one with the duck bill:
We see there before us
A living and breathing
EDMONTOSAURUS!'

A **TRICERATOPS** lurking
Just by the school gate,
Peered into the playground
With eyes cold as slate.

The kids in the playground
Went into a spin
And, screaming in terror,
Came rushing back in.

Said Mortimer Keene,
'There's no cause for alarm.
They are plant-eaters mostly;
They'll do us no harm.'

'No harm?' Mr Singh
Bawled out in a rage.
'We seem to be lost
In the **DINOSAUR AGE!**'

Outside the window,
Someone went, 'Eek!'
It was Emily Bruce
In a **PTEROSAUR'S** beak!

'Mortimer! Save her!'
Loud came the cry
As the **PTEROSAUR** whisked her up

into the sky.

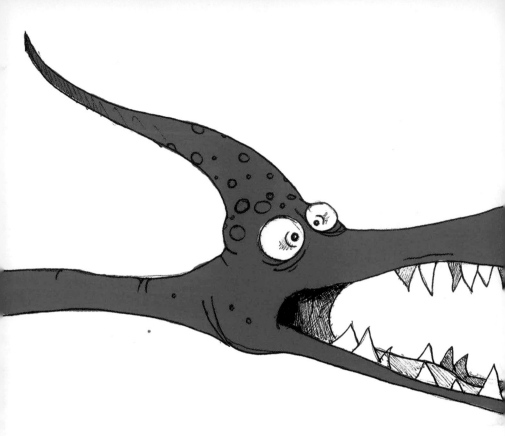

'I'm on it!' cried Mortimer,
And cool as ice,
Reached out a hand
For his stunner device.

He took aim and fired
At the **PTEROSAUR'S** beak -
Which instantly opened
To let out a shriek.

Emily dropped
From its jaws and fell free,
Landing unhurt
In a tall ginkgo tree.

'Phew!' breathed a teacher;
Another cried, 'Yay!'
'Mr Hart, we must fetch her!'
Said Mrs Moray.

They tiptoed outside,
Making barely a sound,
For lumbering dinosaurs
Lurked all around.

At the edge of the forest
More eyes seemed to peer
From the shadowy trees
And they shivered with fear.

'I think I can see her,'
Breathed Mrs Moray.
'My child, are you safe?
We are right on our way!'

'I'm fine,' answered Emily,
'Just grazed my knee.'
And yelling, 'Geronimo!'
Jumped from the tree.

'Shush! Keep your voice down!
The dinosaurs may
Discover our presence,'
Hissed Mrs Moray.

'I see no more dinosaurs,'
Mr Hart said,
'Perhaps we have scared them.
They seem to have fled.'

'I think **that's** what scared them,'
Said Mrs Moray
In a voice that was loaded
With fear and dismay.

Huge and horrific,
Its eyes full of hate,
A **TYRANNOSAURUS**
Loomed over the gate!

Its claws were like knives,
And it drooled from the chops
As it hungrily lurched at
The **TRICERATOPS.**

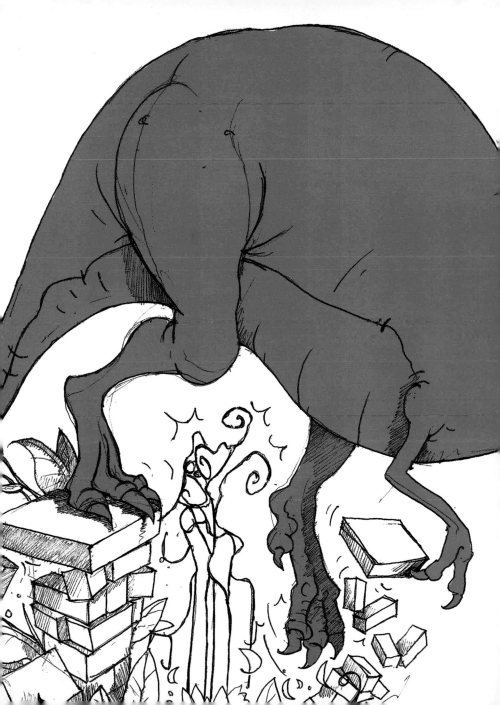

Those in the lab
Heard a terrified **ROAR.**
Then Anthony Lewis
Burst in through the door,

Yelling, 'Do something, Mortimer,
Do something quick!'
And Oliver Morris
Was suddenly sick.

More dinosaurs, eager
For something to munch,
Lumbered up to the school
As if hoping for lunch.

'Get us back in the building!'
Shrieked out Mr Hart.
'Get us back into school
Or they'll tear us apart!'

Mortimer Keene
Went down on all fours
As he rummaged around
In his old cupboard drawers.

'Here's my new grabber net.
Risky, I know
(I've not used it before).
But let's give it a go.'

PTEROSAUR squadrons
Now darkened the sky
As Mortimer Keene
Let the grabber net fly.

It shot through the air
Neatly netting the three:
Mr Hart, the head teacher
And brave Emily.

Mortimer tapped
On a button marked 'GRAB',
And in no time at all
They were back in the lab!

But **PTEROSAURS** now
Were zooming in fast.
One flew at the window
And just missed the glass.

In a minute or two
They'd smash up the school!
Mortimer switched on
His Dark Matter fuel.

And something went

FOOMF!

And the lab again sank
Into the vortex,
And then, all went blank…

'Home again! Home again!'
Cried Mr Green,
Looking out over
A comforting scene

Of houses and cars.
No dinosaurs there,
Only buses and street lamps
And grey pigeons, where

The **PTEROSAUR** menace
Once darkened the sky.
'It's good to be back,'
Someone said with a sigh.

Then Emily passed
Something small from her hand
To Mortimer Keene
Who whispered, 'That's grand!'

'It may turn out to be
A quite fabulous find;
The only one ever
Yet known of its kind!'

And Mortimer started
To sidle away.
'What's that you're holding?'
Asked Mrs Moray.

'Open your hand
And show me, I beg.'
In Mortimer's hand
Was a **PTEROSAUR'S** egg!

Said the schoolgirl: 'It fell
From a nest in the tree…'
The head teacher cried, 'Mortimer!
Give that to me!'

'I'll also take charge of that
Dark Matter fuel.
It has no place at all
At St Barnabas School!'

'But you've both been so brave,'
She finished at last,
'Let's call the whole nightmare
A Thing of the Past.'

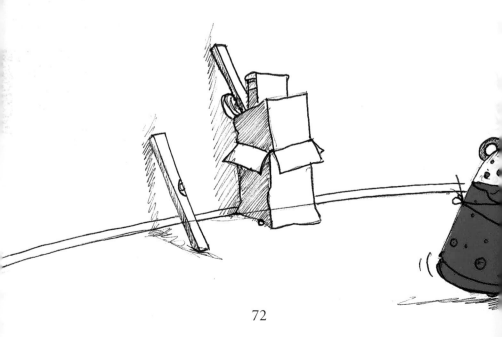

'A Thing of the Past,'
Agreed Mr Green.

'Let's look to the future!'
Said Mortimer Keene.

Following these events
the pterosaur's egg was
deposited at London Zoo
for scientific investigation.
Mortimer's Dark Matter fuel is
under scrutiny at the California
Institute of Technology.

Mortimer's
TIME MACHINE PLAN

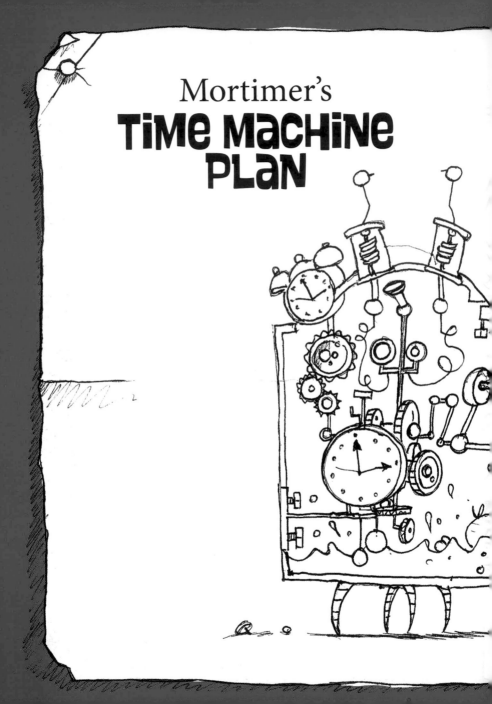

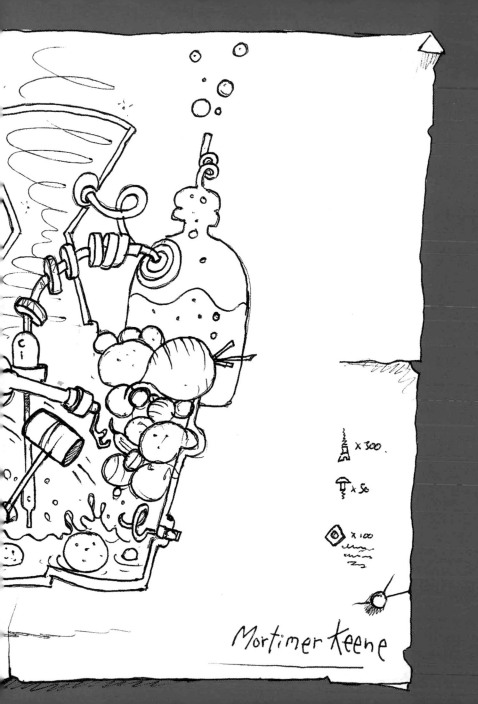

x 300.

x 50

x 100

Mortimer Keene

Mortimer's
TiME MaCHiNE

Wormhole
Detector

Dark Matter
Switch

Machine Powered
by Old Washing
Machine

Time Selection
Device

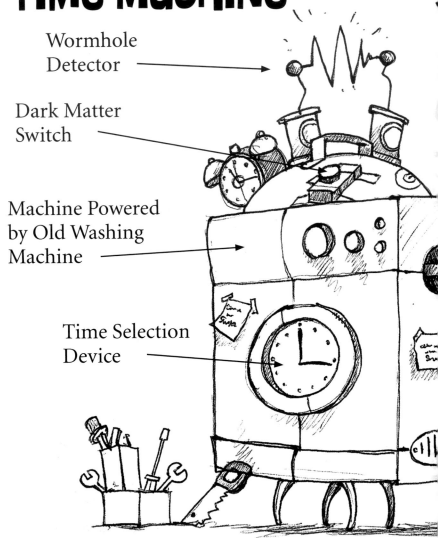

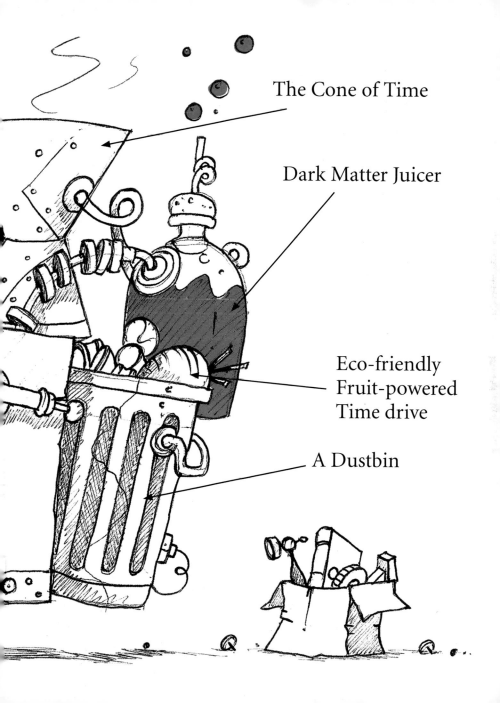

The Cone of Time

Dark Matter Juicer

Eco-friendly
Fruit-powered
Time drive

A Dustbin

A-Z OF DINOSAURS

ANKYLOSAURUS - huge, plant-eating dinosaur with a club-like tail for whacking predators.

BRAINY - nope, dinosaurs weren't very brainy. The brain of a 5-ton stegosaurus was only the size of a walnut.

CARNIVORE - flesh-eating creatures are known as carnivores.

DiNOSauRS - scary reptiles that lived on Earth millions of years ago.

EDMONTOSauRUS - massive, plant-eating dinosaur with a mouth like a duck's bill.

FOSSiLS - remains preserved in rock. Fossilized bones, eggs and even footprints of dinosaurs have survived millions of years.

GiNKGO - one of the oldest types of tree. Ginkgos were around in dinosaur times.

HERBIVORE - plant-eating creatures are known as herbivores.

IGUANODON - large plant-eating dinosaur, with a thumb spike like a tin-opener!

JURASSIC PARK - famous old film about dinosaurs. Warning: it's scary!

K-T EXTINCTION - global catastrophe 65 million years ago. This caused many plant and animal species to die out, including the dinosaurs.

LARGEST DINOSAUR - the plant-eating argentinosaurus from South America was the height of a 6-storey building.

MAMMALS - are warm-blooded creatures that grow hair and suckle their young. There were some mammals around in dinosaur times, but they were tiny, mouse-like creatures.

NYASASAURUS - probably the oldest dinosaur yet found. Scientists have found fossils dating back 240 million years.

OLDEST DINOSAUR - duh? I've just said it was a nyasasaurus.

PTEROSAUR - prehistoric flying reptile. Strictly speaking, pterosaurs weren't dinosaurs and they weren't birds, either!

QUETZALCOATLUS - biggest of the pterosaurs. Its wingspan of up to 15 metres made it the largest flying creature ever.

RAPTOR - means 'Seizer'. The raptors of dinosaur times were smallish flesh-eaters, and mostly feathered.

SPINOSAURUS - was the largest flesh-eating dinosaur – even bigger than T-rex.

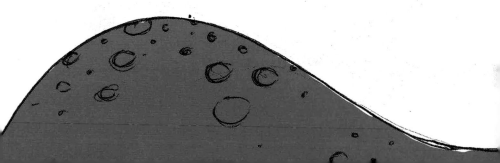

T-ReX - short for tyrannosaurus rex. Massive, flesh-eating dinosaur whose name means 'tyrant lizard king'!

UGLY - how most dinosaurs looked. Let's be honest.

VeLOCiRaPTOR - speedy, vicious, flesh-eating dinosaur, about the size of a turkey.

WOW! - typical response to reading about dinosaurs.

Xenoceratops, Xiaosaurus, Xixianykus ... loads of dinosaur names begin with an X.

Yikes! - typical response to reading about a spinosaurus.

Zalambdalestes - tiny, mouse-like mammal around at the time of the dinosaurs.

MORTIMER'S FUN FACTS ABOUT DINOSAURS

WHERE DID THE DINOSAURS GO? Some of them died out, but some of them turned into birds! At least, scientists think so.

THE BRONTOSAURUS NEVER EXISTED! In fact, it came from a mistake in a single dinosaur skeleton. A scientist accidentally put the skull of one plant-eater onto the skeleton of another plant-eater!

MICROPACHYCEPHALOSAURUS is the dinosaur with the longest name. It has 23 letters and means 'tiny thick-headed lizard'.

DINOSAUR POO Pieces of fossilized dung are called coprolites. Bits of fish or animal bone in dinosaurs' coprolites tell us a lot about what they were eating.

NASTIEST NAME The name of the Stygimoloch means 'horned demon from the river of hell'. Actually, this dinosaur was a harmless plant-eater!

FOOTPRINTS

The biggest of all dinosaurs were plant-eaters like brachiosaurus. They had legs like pillars and left huge footprints like this one on the right.

Draw one on a sheet of A4 paper.

The biggest dinosaur footprints ever found by fossil-hunters measured up to 2 metres long. To draw one full size, get a sheet of paper and… forget it. They don't make paper that big! Get a tape measure and check out what 2 metres looks like. Yup, they were that big!

EGGSTRAORDINARY DINOSAURS

Dinosaurs laid eggs.

Make your own gruesome dinosaur eggs!

Do this with an adult.

YOU NEED: eggs; very strong black coffee/red cabbage/onion skins (or use special egg-dying colours if you like); pinch of salt; 2 tbs vinegar.

WHAT YOU DO: hard boil the eggs, adding any one of the suggestions above to the water, plus vinegar and salt. Allow to stand until the colour has deepened. Interestingly, red cabbage makes the eggs go blue, not red!

ATTACK of the
SLIME!

Tim Healey and
Chris Mould

978 0 340 99773 4

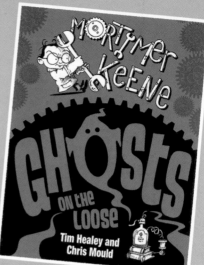

GHOSTS
ON THE
LOOSE

Tim Healey and
Chris Mould

978 0 340 99774 1

978 0 340 99775 8

978 1 444 91969 1

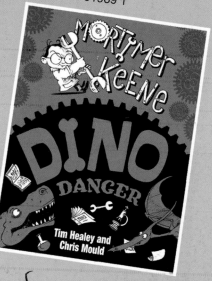

Look out for these other **CRAZY** Mortimer Books!